EUROPE
Geography Activity Book

Maps, Facts, Flags, Activities:
Learn About the Countries of Europe

Europe is one of the seven continents. Located entirely in the Northern Hemisphere, it is the second smallest continent with an area of approximately 3.93 million square miles (or 10.18 million square kilometers). It is made up of 51 countries (with seven of these having land in both Europe and Asia). The total population is about 750 million (as of 2020). Europe is divided into the following regions:

Western Europe, which includes Austria, Belgium, France, Germany, Liechtenstein, Luxembourg, Monaco, Netherlands, and Switzerland

Eastern Europe, which includes Belarus, Bulgaria, Czech Republic, Hungary, Poland, Moldova, Romania, Russia, Slovakia, and Ukraine

Northern Europe, which includes Denmark, Estonia, Finland, Iceland, Ireland, Latvia, Lithuania, Norway, Sweden, and United Kingdom

Southern Europe, which includes Albania, Andorra, Bosnia and Herzegovina, Croatia, Greece, Italy, Malta, Montenegro, North Macedonia, Portugal, San Marino, Serbia, Slovenia, Spain, and Vatican City

The countries of Russia, Turkey, Kazakhstan, Azerbaijan, Georgia, Armenia, and Cyprus have territory in both Asia and Europe.

Europe is a continent of diversity. There are twenty-four official languages and as many as 200 other languages spoken across the countries of Europe. While Christianity is the dominant religion, others such as Judaism and Islam are common and about 20 percent of the population does not identify with any religion. In addition to language and religion, Europe is diverse in its people, cuisines, cultures, and climate.

European countries included in this book:

1. Albania
2. Andorra
3. Armenia
4. Austria
5. Azerbaijan
6. Belarus
7. Belgium
8. Bosnia and Herzegovina
9. Bulgaria
10. Croatia
11. Cyprus
12. Czech Republic (Czechia)
13. Denmark
14. Estonia
15. Finland
16. France
17. Georgia
18. Germany
19. Greece
20. Hungary
21. Iceland
22. Ireland
23. Italy
24. Kazakhstan
25. Kosovo
26. Latvia
27. Liechtenstein
28. Lithuania
29. Luxembourg
30. Malta
31. Moldova
32. Monaco
33. Montenegro
34. Netherlands
35. North Macedonia
36. Norway
37. Poland
38. Portugal
39. Romania
40. Russian Federation
41. San Marino
42. Serbia
43. Slovakia
44. Slovenia
45. Spain
46. Sweden
47. Switzerland
48. Turkey
49. Ukraine
50. United Kingdom
51. Vatican City (Holy See)

Color the Countries!

Color the map of Europe below and then
use the map to answer the questions

1. How many countries are also islands? _____

2. Which is the largest country in Europe? _____

3. How many countries are landlocked? _____

4. Which countries begin with the letter F? _____

5. Which is the northern most country? _____

ALBANIA

National Motto: You, Albania, give me honor, give me the name Albanian

MONTENEGRO

KOSOVO

Tropojë

Shkodër   Kukës

Shëngjin

Lezhë   Peshkopi

MACEDONIA

TIRANA

Durrës

ALBANIA

Adriatic Sea   Elbasan

Lushnjë

Pogradec

Fier

Berat   Korçë

Vlorë

Tepelenë

ITALY   Gjirokastër   GREECE

Strait of Otranto   Sarandë

Butrint

Facts About Albania

Capital: Tirana

Area: 11,100 square miles (28,748 square kilometers)

Major Cities: Durres, Elbasen, Vlore

Population: 4,802,740

Bordering Countries: Montenegro, Kosovo, North Macedonia, Greece

Language: Albanian

Major Landmarks: Osum Gorge, Langarica Canyon, Lake Ohrid

Famous Albanians: Frederik Ndoci (artist), Fadil Berisha (photographer)

Find the Words

```
F L B G R U P B E A M H
V G A J R E I G X N O E
U S N K R Y R E E P T B
Y U D O E O F S Z E H A
M A L U G O A U V P E L
Y V L M R B H K A Q R K
B R U B L R L R C G T A
P S M E A C E R I E E N
O T I G U N Z S Y D R S
U L X J X I I D V I E Q
T I R A N A Y A P G S V
R L A N G A R I C A A S
```

ALBANIA	LANGARICA
BALKANS	MOTHER TERESA
DURRES	OSUM GORGE
ELBASEN	TIRANA
LAKE OHRID	VLORE

Country Flag

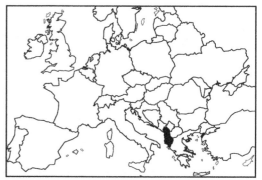

ANDORRA

National Motto: Strength united is stronger

FRANCE

El Serrat

ANDORRA

Soldeu

ANDORRA
LA VELLA

Encamp

Les Escaldes

Sant Julià
de Lòria

SPAIN

Facts About Andorra

Capital: Andorra La Vella

Area: 181 square miles (470 square kilometers)

Major Cities: Escaldes-Engordany, Encamp

Population: 77,265

Bordering Countries: Spain, France

Language: Catalan

Major Landmarks: Casa de la Vall, Centro Historico

Famous Andorrans: Antoni Bernadó (Olympic athlete) , Marc Vales (soccer player)

Find the Words

M	C	P	M	O	U	N	T	A	I	N	S
Y	A	R	W	M	C	I	A	A	F	G	Y
G	S	I	Y	C	A	N	P	O	Q	T	Z
A	A	N	R	A	T	D	Y	R	A	U	B
N	D	C	O	N	A	E	R	D	U	C	O
D	E	I	M	I	L	P	E	I	Y	D	B
O	L	P	E	L	A	E	N	N	D	X	P
R	A	A	R	L	N	N	E	O	D	G	Z
R	V	L	O	O	D	D	E	V	N	S	Z
A	A	I	L	I	F	E	S	I	L	N	Z
W	L	T	F	O	L	N	V	E	R	T	F
V	L	Y	X	V	B	T	C	B	I	I	D

ANDORRA   MOUNTAINS
CANILLO   ORDINO
CASA DE LA VALL PRINCIPALITY
CATALAN   PYRENEES
INDEPENDENT   ROMERO

Country Flag

ARMENIA

National Motto: One Nation, One Culture

Facts About Armenia

Capital: Yerevan

Area: 11,484 square miles (29,743 square kilometers)

Major Cities: Gyumri, Vanadzor

Population: 2,970,404

Bordering Countries: Georgia, Azerbaijan, Iran, Turkey

Language: Armenian

Major Landmarks: Geghard Monastery, Tatev Monastery, Khor Virab

Famous Armenians: Levon Aronian (chess player), Sirusho (singer)

Find the Words

```
A K G A R M A V I R J B
R H G Y Z T F A S Y S J
M O W P U U H T G E Q N
E R J D O M A Z I H A K
N V V Q I G R R L V L J
I I F A A A E I E V H D
A R J R N T S R P I A U
N A A C S A E P U I T D
G B H A T Y D L O P K I
D L N J D L G Z B R R L
H O L Q I B D U O Y A M
M O T T O M A N S R D T
```

ARAGATS	KHOR VIRAB
ARMAVIR	MONASTERIES
ARMENIAN	OTTOMANS
DIASPORA	VANADZOR
GYUMRI	YEREVAN

Country Flag

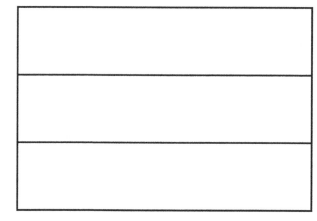

AUSTRIA

National Motto: No official motto

Facts About Austria

Capital: Vienna

Area: 32,386 square miles (83,879 square kilometers)

Major Cities: Vienna, Salzburg, Graz

Population: 9,006,398

Bordering Countries: Czech Republic, Germany, Slovakia, Hungary, Slovenia, Italy, Switzerland, Liechterstein

Language: German

Major Landmarks: Clock Tower, Hallstatt Old Town, Hofburg Palace

Famous Austrians: Joseph Haydn (composer), Karl Popper (philosopher)

Find the Words

Q	B	V	P	E	Z	Q	P	E	R	O	U
A	O	L	D	T	O	W	N	E	E	E	U
L	B	A	I	G	Z	Z	W	K	S	A	J
P	H	D	U	A	F	O	Q	R	A	S	G
S	K	A	R	S	T	J	I	L	L	I	E
J	M	G	L	K	T	G	X	Y	Z	D	R
D	W	B	C	L	R	R	A	S	B	R	M
H	Q	O	X	U	S	W	I	H	U	K	A
J	L	J	B	G	F	T	U	A	R	L	N
C	W	F	V	S	I	T	A	A	G	A	S
D	O	X	C	X	V	S	W	T	I	G	A
H	Q	V	I	E	N	N	A	J	T	Q	M

ALPS	HALLSTATT
AUSTRIA	HOFBURG
CLOCK TOWER	OLD TOWN
GERMAN	SALZBURG
GRAZ	VIENNA

Country Flag

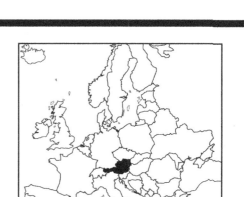

AZERBAIJAN

National Motto: The Land of Fire

Facts About Azerbaijan

Capital: Baku

Area: 33,436 square miles (86,600 square kilometers)

Major Cities: Ganja, Sumqayit, Mingecevir

Population: 10,139,177

Bordering Countries: Russia, Georgia, Iran, Turkey, Armenia

Language: Azerbaijani

Major Landmarks: Icherisheher, Maiden Tower, Heydar Aliyev Centre, Gobustan National Park

Famous Azerbaijans: Garry Kasparov (chess player), Lev Landau (physicist)

Find the Words

R	W	M	W	M	B	O	C	A	I	E	F
M	I	O	U	A	V	Z	A	Z	N	C	Y
Y	A	U	R	I	U	Z	U	E	N	A	T
K	A	N	S	D	M	Z	C	R	E	S	H
J	Z	T	U	E	H	U	A	B	R	P	Z
U	J	A	M	N	D	Y	S	A	C	I	K
O	B	I	Q	T	B	B	U	I	I	A	S
Y	B	N	A	O	A	J	S	J	T	N	Y
G	O	S	Y	W	K	K	K	A	Y	S	L
F	A	P	I	E	U	F	Z	N	R	E	D
Y	Y	E	T	R	G	A	N	J	A	A	K
I	C	H	E	R	I	S	H	E	H	E	R

AZERBAIJAN   ICHERISHEHER
BAKU   INNER CITY
CASPIAN SEA   MAIDEN TOWER
CAUCASUS   MOUNTAINS
GANJA   SUMQAYIT

Country Flag

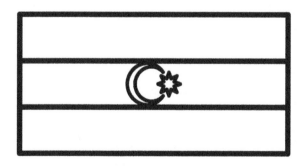

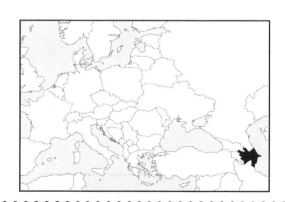

BELARUS

National Motto: Long Live Belarus!

LATVIA

LITHUANIA

RUSSIA

Polotsk

Vitebsk

Orsha

MINSK

Mogilev

Grodno

Neman

POLAND

Baranovichi

Babruysk

Dnieper

BELARUS

Gomel

Brest

Pinsk

Prypiat

Mazyr

UKRAINE

Facts About Belarus

Capital: Minsk

Area: 80,200 square miles (207,600 square kilometers)

Major Cities: Grodno, Gomel, Mogilev

Population: 9,449,323

Bordering Countries: Poland, Lithuania, Latvia, Russia, Ukraine

Language: Belarusian, Russian

Major Landmarks: Kosava Castle, Brest Fortress, Bialowieza Forest

Famous Belarusians: Marc Chagall (artist), Lev Vygotsky (psychologist)

Find the Words

E	R	G	M	X	K	E	N	E	D	O	U
X	U	O	E	O	S	O	L	W	N	H	X
B	S	M	B	L	G	T	S	D	B	B	K
E	S	E	G	R	S	I	O	A	E	L	M
L	I	L	D	A	E	R	L	K	V	X	C
A	A	I	C	D	G	S	Y	E	L	A	K
R	N	K	O	S	M	G	T	L	R	U	Z
U	R	L	A	N	D	L	O	C	K	E	D
S	Q	Y	E	I	H	M	M	C	U	Z	N
I	U	R	A	D	Z	I	W	I	L	L	L
A	T	H	B	F	D	I	J	Q	U	D	U
N	P	N	B	C	O	W	Z	Q	N	K	U

BELARUSIAN   KOSAVA
BREST   LANDLOCKED
CASTLE   MOGILER
GOMEL   RADZIWILL
GRODNO   RUSSIAN

Country Flag

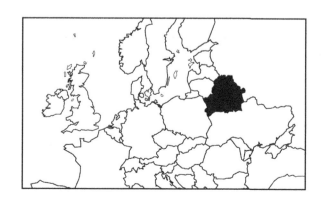

BELGIUM

National Motto: *Unity makes strength*

Facts About Belgium

Capital: Brussels

Area: 11,849 square miles (30,689 square kilometers)

Major Cities: Brussels, Bruges, Antwerp

Population: 11,589,623

Bordering Countries: Netherlands, Germany, Luxembourg, France

Language: Dutch, French, German

Major Landmarks: Grand Palace, Canal du Centre

Famous Belgians: Charlemagne (king), Jean-Claude Van Damme (martial arts)

Find the Words

```
V C P B R U S S E L S E
L H K B D A F V E I R Z
Z O I F I R N Q Y U W V
T C N C A L Y T T O S K
P O G W H O I C W E C N
K L D X K G E N L E S R
H A O R I T B R G L R P
W T M E I Y A Y A U K P
S E F H N H X N X I A K
G P C O C E A N L O L L
I R L E E C B R U G E S
A G R A N D P A L A C E
```

ANTWERP	CANALS
ARCHITECTURE	CHARLES V
BILINGUAL	CHOCOLATE
BRUGES	GRAND PALACE
BRUSSELS	KINGDOM

Country Flag

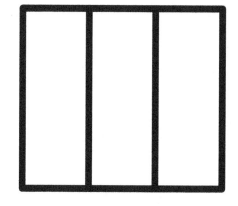

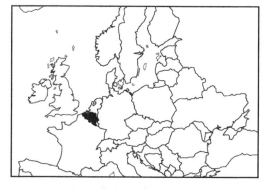

BOSNIA AND HERZEGOVINA

National Motto: No official motto

CROATIA

Prijedor

Bihać

Banja
Luka

Brčko

Tuzla

SERBIA

**BOSNIA AND
HERZEGOVINA**

Zenica

CROATIA

SARAJEVO

Goražde

Mostar

Adriatic Sea

CROATIA

MONTENEGRO

Facts About Bosnia and Herzegovina

Capital: Sarajevo

Area: 19,767 square miles (51,200 square kilometers)

Major Cities: Sarajevo, Banja Luka, Tuzla

Population: 3,280,819

Bordering Countries: Croatia, Serbia, Montenegro

Language: Croatian, Bosnian, Serbian

Major Landmarks: Old Bridge, Kravica Waterfall, Stari Most

Famous Bosnians: Goran Bregović (musician), Ivo Andric (writer)

Find the Words

```
V T U Z L A J O B H M J
H E R Z E G O V I N A S
K S B O Q G O T A T P S
H T A J L D Q I S L R A
L A I B W D N G A L A R
Q R N K A S B C E C O A
D I X M O L I R I U O J
E M T B W R K V I H Y E
W O J D A I A A Q D F V
I S N N Q R J C N X G O
X T I Y K B H K P S O E
C D P D K T R A V N I K
```

BALKANS   OLD BRIDGE
BOSNIA   SARAJEVO
DINARIC ALPS   STARI MOST
HERZEGOVINA   TRAVNIK
KRAVICA   TUZLA

Country Flag

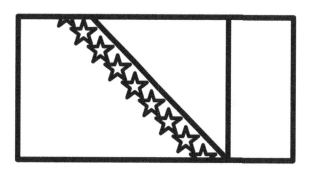

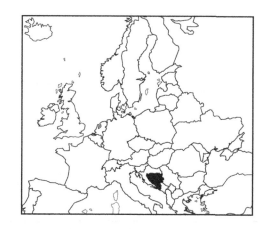

BULGARIA

National Motto: Unity Makes Strength

Facts About Bulgaria

Capital: Sofia

Area: 42,855 square miles (110,879 square kilometers)

Major Cities: Plovdiv, Varna, Burgas

Population: 6,948,445

Bordering Countries: Greece, Macedonia, Romania, Serbia

Language: Bulgarian

Major Landmarks: Monastery of Saint Ivan of Rila, Sunny Beach, Aladzha Monastery

Famous Bulgarians: Nina Dobrev (actress), Grigor Dimitrov (tennis player)

Find the Words

```
S Z U S M B F H H V W D
H U W V I Y R W O S E N
B S N K I L P K N B P P
L O T N V T H O U M S L
A F O Y Y C O N L L Q O
C I M O I B A S H Q V V
K A M O E D E J H L Z D
S D T G A U Y A W A R I
E S T F E X D G C I Q R
A B U R G A S Q H H V Q
W U L S A I N T I V A N
X L L V A R N A X E Z Q
```

BLACK SEA	SOFIA
BURGAS	STOICHKOV
DANUBE	SUNNY BEACH
PLOVDIR	VARNA
SAINT IVAN	VITOSHA

Country Flag

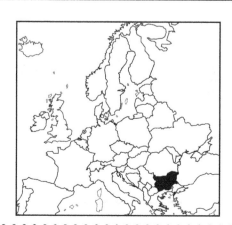

CROATIA

National Motto: God and Croats

Facts About Croatia

Capital: Zagreb

Area: 21,851 square miles (56,594 square kilometers)

Major Cities: Dubrovnik, Zadar, Split

Population: 4,105,267

Bordering Countries: Hungary, Serbia, Bosnia and Herzegovina, Montenegro, Slovenia

Language: Croatian

Major Landmarks: Plitvice Lakes, Diocletian's Palace, Krka National Park

Famous Croatians: Nikola Tesla (inventor), Rudolf Steiner (philosopher)

Find the Words

A	J	A	C	R	O	A	T	I	A	N	B
S	M	G	I	Z	H	O	L	G	R	A	P
S	K	P	H	Z	L	S	D	J	N	L	K
W	R	A	H	W	A	B	P	R	O	I	U
A	K	D	D	I	K	G	A	L	N	C	P
Y	A	R	H	Z	T	D	R	V	I	A	W
J	P	I	Q	F	A	H	O	E	L	T	C
T	A	A	F	Z	J	R	E	U	L	K	G
S	R	T	C	W	B	Z	P	A	P	O	M
U	K	I	I	U	W	B	Q	U	T	D	P
T	G	C	D	P	O	B	T	P	L	E	S
T	O	M	I	S	L	A	V	X	L	Y	R

ADRIATIC   PULA

AMPHITHEATER   SPLIT

CROATIAN   TOMISLAV

DUBROVNIK   ZADAR

KRKA PARK   ZAGRELO

Country Flag

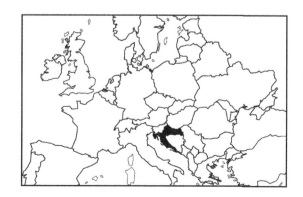

CYPRUS

National Motto: No official motto

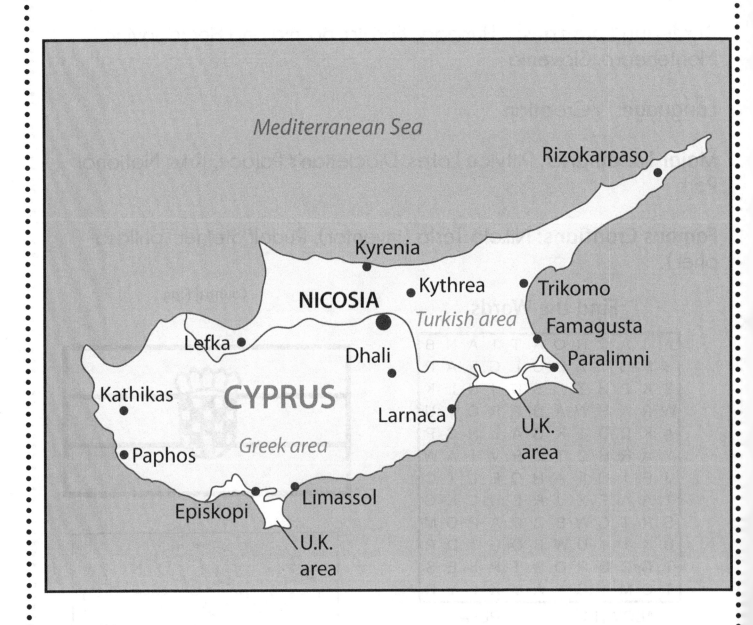

Facts About Cyprus

Capital: Nicosia

Area: 3,572 square miles (9,251 square kilometers)

Major Cities: Larnaca, Limassol, Paphos

Population: 1,207,359

Neighboring Countries: Turkey, Syria, Lebanon, Israel, Egypt, Greece

Language: Greek, Turkish

Major Landmarks: Petra tou Romiou, Nissi Beach, Tombs of the Kings, Kykkos Monastery

Famous Cyprians: Marcos Baghdatis (tennis player), Simon Fuller (TV personality), Makarios III (president)

Find the Words

L	P	C	O	M	C	T	A	P	Z	I	D
A	A	P	Y	M	A	I	U	O	N	N	D
N	P	Z	X	R	S	K	I	R	A	X	K
A	H	U	U	O	P	G	A	L	K	E	I
T	O	V	C	R	R	U	S	R	E	E	W
O	S	I	Q	Y	A	I	S	R	I	H	Y
L	N	J	D	P	W	P	G	Y	I	O	Y
I	N	I	S	S	I	B	E	A	C	H	S
A	F	I	P	I	C	H	O	K	V	L	L
N	X	O	I	J	U	E	A	C	S	I	N
Q	N	C	P	J	A	C	J	V	Z	H	I
G	J	Q	B	L	A	R	N	A	C	A	B

ANATOLIAN   MAKARIOS
CYRPUS   NICOSIA
GREEK   NISSI BEACH
ISLAND   PAPHOS
LARNACA   TURKEY

Country Flag

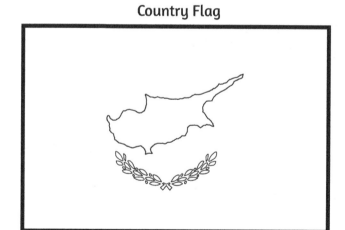

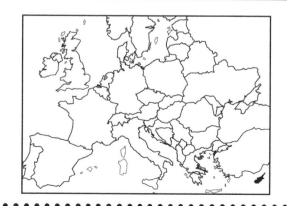

CZECH REPUBLIC

National Motto: Truth prevails

Facts About Czech Republic

Capital: Prague

Area: 30,452 square miles (78,867 square kilometers)

Major Cities: Prague, Brno, Ostrava

Population: 10,708,981

Bordering Countries: Poland, Germany, Austria, Slovakia

Language: Czech

Major Landmarks: Prague Castle, Charles Bridge, St. Vitus Cathedral

Famous Czechs: Martina Navratilova (tennis player), Rainer Maria Rilke (author), Gregor Mendel (scientist), Charles IV (emperor)

Find the Words

```
R J P X L M O R A V I A
X E I E W Q C L A X P Q
J J P N U U Z N C T D M
E B O U O U U Q A W P F
J D O M B R Y O T R R W
M U O H O L I B H T A Z
I L E K E L I Y E K G J
O W B K A M J C D O U U
S C R T A P I P R I E M
Y W N M O F O A A D T F
I S O S U Y K R L H D J
C A S T L E S A S L U L
```

BOHEMIA   KORUNA
BRNO   MORAVIA
CASTLES   OLOMOUC
CATHEDRALS   PRAGUE
KAFKA   REPUBLIC

Country Flag

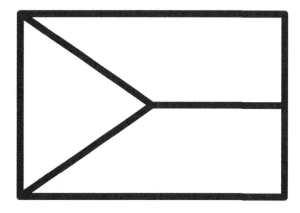

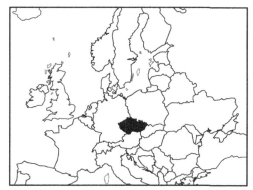

DENMARK

National Motto: God's help, the love of the people, Denmark's strength

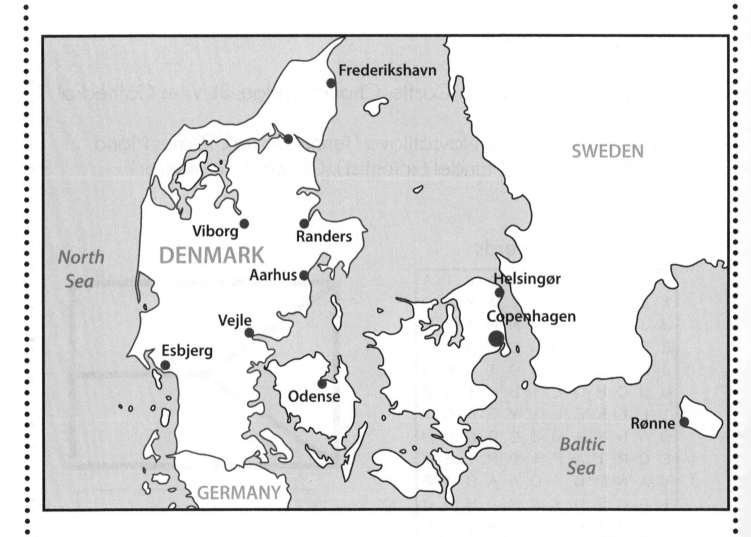

Facts About Denmark

Capital: Copenhagen

Area: 16,577 square miles (42,943 square kilometers)

Major Cities: Aarhus, Odense, Aalborg

Population: 5,792,202

Neighboring Countries: Germany, Norway, Sweden

Language: Danish

Major Landmarks: Tivoli Gardens, The Little Mermaid, Kronberg

Famous Danes: Søren Kierkegaard (philosopher), Hans Christian Andersen (author), Jacob Riis (journalist)

Find the Words

```
F O N H W A G E S A N B
J Z E J D H J U R E N G
Z T J A C A H P G Y Y Y
R R I I N R N A K M H A
T A R V A D H I T P A D
U L Z A O N E Q S S V E
U W T P E L I R C H N N
F K Y P T J I F S R K M
B E O F J R J K S E A A
H C I E Y Q E C E C N R
K O D E N S E O K D Z K
W G A A L B O R G G K P
```

AALBORG	DENMARK
AARHUS	NYHAVN
ANDERSEN	ODENSE
COPENHAGEN	TIVOLI
DANISH	ULRICH

Country Flag

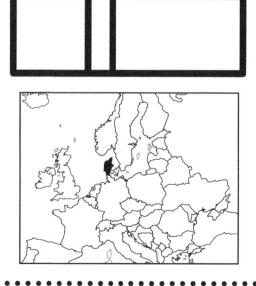

ESTONIA

National Motto: No official motto.

FINLAND

Gulf of Finland

Baltic Sea

Paldiski
Muuga
Kunda
Narva
TALLINN
Kohtla-Järve

Hiiumaa
Haapsalu
Paide
Lake Peipus

ESTONIA

Saaremaa
Pärnu
Viljandi
Tartu

Valga

Gulf of Riga
RUSSIA

LATVIA

Facts About Estonia

Capital: Tallinn

Area: 17,505 square miles (45,227 square kilometers)

Major Cities: Tartu, Narva

Population: 1,326,535

Bordering Countries: Russia, Latvia

Language: Estonian

Major Landmarks: Alexander Nevsky Cathedral, Kumu, Lahemaa National Park

Famous Estonians: Louis Kahn (architect), Wolfgang Köhler (psychologist)

Find the Words

```
G O J C V C X W Y V W A
F I B E J T F M U F S M
Z F A S Z L J T N D K V
O O L T Z O N N H N Q
S L T O T E L A A N D A
B Z I N J A L D I R W P
N U C I L S R L T U V O
Q Y A A I J L T M O Q A
N S O N P A A U U B W G
F Q V M T X K G J U P N
D L B L E N U S A D A M
F O R E S T S W G F N D
```

BALTIC	LENUSADAM
ESTONIAN	NARVA
FORESTS	OLD TOWN
ISLANDS	TALLINN
KUMU	TARTU

Country Flag

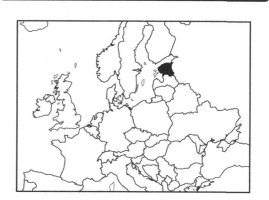

FINLAND

National Motto: No official motto.

Facts About Finland

Capital: Helsinki

Area: 130,672 square miles (338,455 square kilometers)

Major Cities: Tampere, Turku, Oulu

Population: 5,540,720

Bordering Countries: Norway, Russia, Sweden

Language: Finnish, Swedish

Major Landmarks: Suomenlinna Fortress, Helsinki Cathedral, Turku Castle

Famous Finns: Jean Sibelius (composer), Linus Torvalds (computer programmer)

Find the Words

M	E	V	W	N	F	G	F	N	Y	X	Y
S	A	U	N	A	S	F	Z	D	S	G	S
W	Y	H	U	B	N	B	C	Q	A	F	C
S	U	O	M	E	N	L	I	N	N	A	A
H	H	T	C	T	O	J	H	H	V	S	N
B	E	I	L	Z	U	S	L	V	T	E	D
T	H	L	U	A	I	R	P	R	R	A	I
D	S	L	S	N	P	Y	K	E	P	R	N
C	U	M	N	I	Z	L	P	U	V	C	A
O	D	I	D	J	N	M	A	I	Y	T	V
M	F	W	H	S	A	K	M	N	K	I	I
V	P	I	W	T	F	Q	I	K	D	C	A

ARCTIC   SAUNAS
FINNISH   SCANDINAVIA
HELSINKI   SUOMENLINNA
LAPLAND   TAMPERE
OULU   TURKU

Country Flag

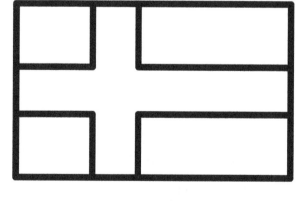

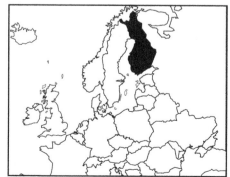

FRANCE

National Motto: Liberty, equality, fraternity

UNITED KINGDOM

NETHERLANDS

GERMANY

BELGIUM

LUXEMBOURG

Calais

English Channel

Cherbourg

Le Havre

Rouen

Reims

Nancy

PARIS

Epernay

Strasbourg

Brest

Bayeux

Dinard

St Malo

Angers

Orleans

Dijon

SWITZERLAND

Nantes

ATLANTIC
OCEAN

FRANCE

Lyon

Aix-les-Bains

ITALY

Grenoble

Bordeaux

Bay of Biscay

Cahors

Aix-en-Provence

MONACO

Avignon

Arles

Nice

Biarritz

Toulouse

Montpellier

Cannes

Pau

Marseille

St Tropez

Lourdes

Corsica

SPAIN

ANDORRA

Ajaccio

Mediterranean Sea

Facts About France

Capital: Paris

Area: 244,300 square miles (551,500 square kilometers)

Major Cities: Marseille, Lyon, Strasbourg

Population: 65,273,511

Bordering Countries: Belgium, Luxembourg, Germany, Switzerland, Italy, Spain, Andorra

Language: French

Major Landmarks: Eiffel Tower, Louvre Museum, Palace of Versailles, Notre-Dame Cathedral

Famous French: Napoleon Bonaparte (military commander), Louis XIV (king), Voltaire (author), René Descartes (philosopher)

Find the Words

M	A	Z	O	E	T	E	M	S	X	P	Z
A	C	K	C	M	X	I	M	T	D	W	Q
R	U	P	A	N	S	F	N	R	A	T	B
S	B	W	O	N	E	F	Q	A	S	L	A
E	R	Y	O	A	I	E	J	S	W	O	G
I	L	F	G	P	T	L	V	B	A	U	U
L	Q	R	H	O	A	T	W	O	R	V	E
L	T	E	E	L	B	O	D	U	E	R	T
E	M	N	O	E	E	W	C	R	P	E	T
O	G	C	F	O	H	E	Y	G	G	V	E
X	I	H	Y	N	S	R	P	A	R	I	S
V	E	R	S	A	I	L	L	E	S	W	K

BAGUETTE   MARSEILLE
EIFFEL TOWER   NAPOLEON
FRENCH   PARIS
LOUVRE   STRASBOURG
LYON   VERSAILLES

Country Flag

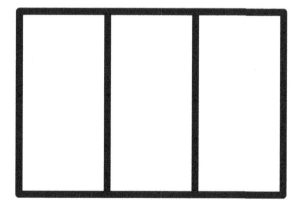

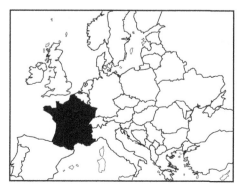

GEORGIA

National Motto: Strength is in Unity!

RUSSIA

Sukhumi

Zugdidi

Kutaisi

Ambrolauri

Black Sea

Poti

GEORGIA

Tskhinvali

Gori

Telavi

TBILISI

Akhaltsikhe

Batumi

Rustavi

Akhalkalaki

Bolnisi

AZERBAIJAN

TURKEY

ARMENIA

Facts About Georgia

Capital: Tbilisi

Area: 26,911 square miles (69,700 square kilometers)

Major Cities: Batumi, Kutaisi, Rustavi

Population: 3,989,167

Bordering Countries: Russia, Azerbaijan, Armenia, Turkey

Language: Georgian

Major Landmarks: Svetitskhoveli Cathedral, Uplistsikhe, Narikala Fortress, Gergeti Trinity Church, Vardzia

Famous Georgians: Sergei Parajanov (director), Katie Melua (musician)

Find the Words

J	W	P	C	B	Y	C	R	H	I	J	S
I	W	K	S	E	L	B	J	M	H	U	P
C	I	G	O	K	N	A	U	O	S	I	I
T	N	E	G	X	U	T	C	A	R	T	X
B	E	O	J	E	A	T	C	K	E	K	S
I	B	R	O	B	C	U	A	H	S	D	A
L	P	G	J	Z	A	V	K	I	Q	E	L
I	K	I	I	C	U	A	I	E	S	B	A
S	Q	A	T	L	K	Q	I	M	E	I	T
I	N	N	N	A	R	I	K	A	L	A	J
W	V	A	R	D	Z	I	A	T	L	U	J
G	W	G	E	X	N	W	J	A	P	D	Q

BATUMI   KUTAISI
BLACK SEA   NARIKALA
CAUCASUS   TBILISI
GEORGIAN   VARDZIA
KAKHETI   WINE

Country Flag

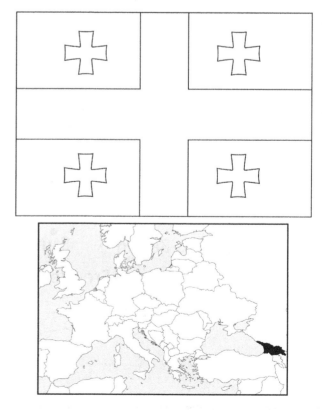

GERMANY

National Motto: Unity and justice and freedom

Facts About Germany

Capital: Berlin

Area: 137,988 square miles (357,022 square kilometers)

Major Cities: Munich, Frankfurt, Hamburg

Population: 83,783,942

Bordering Countries: Denmark, Netherlands, Belgium, Luxembourg, France, Switzerland, Austria, Czech Republic, Poland

Language: German

Major Landmarks: Neuschwanstein Castle, Brandenburg Gate, Berlin Wall, Cologne Cathedral

Famous Germans: Beethoven (composer), Albert Einstein (physicist), Karl Marx (philosopher), Igor Stravinsky (composer)

Find the Words

```
H B F K K I F M M S Z B
Z F R A N K F U R T E R
G E R M A N I Z U P N A
H G L E F T X L G E X N
A E Z S H D H I V B L D
M A I E A C P O B E E E
B R O N I U H F W R K N
U P E N S T S X K L N B
R V U Q E T G A I I S U
G M G E Y R E X G N N R
D I B I N H W I R E V G
A U T O B A H N N Z S Y
```

AUTOBAHN   FRANKFURT
BEETHOVEN   GERMAN
BERLIN   HAMBURG
BRANDENBURG   MUNICH
EINSTEIN   SAUSAGES

Country Flag

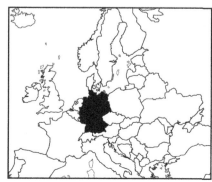

GREECE

National Motto: Freedom or Death

Facts About Greece

Capital: Athens

Area: 50,949 square miles (131,957 square kilometers)

Major Cities: Athens, Thessaloniki, Heraklion

Population: 10,423,054

Bordering Countries: Albania, Bulgaria, North Macedonia, Turkey

Language: Greek

Major Landmarks: The Parthenon, Acropolis, Academy of Athens, Colossus of Rhodes

Famous Greeks: Aristole (philosopher), Alexander the Great (ruler), Homer (author), Hippocrates (physician)

Find the Words

A	R	I	S	T	O	T	L	E	U	I	N
M	P	B	P	P	T	T	D	A	N	O	R
Y	L	H	E	E	M	K	E	R	N	A	S
K	T	M	I	A	B	S	Y	E	F	T	D
O	O	I	A	L	N	U	H	S	H	H	E
N	H	S	S	A	O	T	U	Z	J	E	M
O	E	P	E	L	R	S	V	S	R	N	O
S	I	G	J	A	A	F	O	E	U	S	C
P	E	L	P	A	C	N	M	P	O	I	R
A	N	V	N	U	R	O	D	C	H	P	A
E	N	D	F	Y	H	X	Z	S	L	Y	C
W	A	C	R	O	P	O	L	I	S	B	Y

ACROPOLIS   HOMER
AEGEAN SEA   ISLANDS
ARISTOTLE   MYKONOS
ATHENS   PARTHENON
DEMOCRACY   PHILOSOPHY

Country Flag

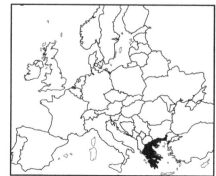

HUNGARY

National Motto: With the help of God for Homeland and Freedom

Facts About Hungary

Capital: Budapest

Area: 35,919 square miles (93,022 square kilometers)

Major Cities: Szeged, Debrecen, Miskolc

Population: 9,660,351

Bordering Countries: Austria, Serbia, Croatia, Slovenia, Romania, Ukraine, Slovakia

Language: Hungarian

Major Landmarks: Buda Castle, Danube River, Széchenyi Medicinal Bath

Famous Hungarians: Harry Houdini (magician), George Soros (investor), John von Neumann (mathmetician)

Find the Words

```
Y W M U S K O L C P S L
B T D Z I J G F P A H A
B U U E D V C H P V U N
V F D Y B A D S O T N D
S K S A W R L E S V G L
Z Y R I C A E E Q W A O
E Z W U R A P C X B R C
G U E E E A S G E O I K
E W N Q D Q K T X N A E
D I K U O N B R L J N D
M H B J B R O D Y E R O
U D A N U B E R I V E R
```

BRODY   HUNGARIAN
BUDA CASTLE   LANDLOCKED
BUDAPEST   MINERAL SPAS
DANUBE RIVER   MUSKOLC
DEBRECEN   SZEGED

Country Flag

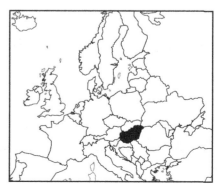

ICELAND

National Motto: No official motto

Facts About Iceland

Capital: Reykjavik

Area: 39,769 square miles (103,125 square kilometers)

Major Cities: Vik, Akureyri, Hafnarfjordur

Population: 341,243

Bordering Countries: None

Language: Icelandic

Major Landmarks: Blue Lagoon, Jokulsarlon Glacier Lagoon, Gullfoss

Famous Icelanders: Leif Ericson (explorer), Bjork (singer)

Find the Words

```
T C I C E L A N D I C W
A X B X G V S D N U T K
S T U L O W H J G M I Q
A H I T U G C X T V I M
V G E E J E E C A J S R
I U X E A S L J I E L J
K L Z L P T K A K W A K
E L F J A Y Y R G H N Y
N F Q Y E V O F Q O D M
V O Q R G J A O X V O G
K S I K B V G Y U Z H N
E S G L A C I E R S A Q
```

BJORK   ISLAND
BLUE LAGOON   LAVA
GLACIERS   REYKJAVIK
GULLFOSS   SHEEP
ICELANDIC   VIK

Country Flag

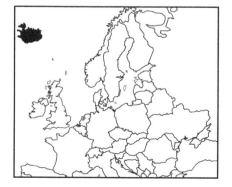

IRELAND

National Motto: Ireland forever

Facts About Ireland

Capital: Dublin

Area: 32,595 square miles (70,273 square kilometers)

Major Cities: Belfast, Cork, Derry

Population: 4,937,786

Bordering Countries: United Kingdom

Language: English and Irish

Major Landmarks: Cliffs of Moher, Belfast Castle, Bangor Cathedral

Famous Irish : C. S. Lewis (author), Bono (musician), William Butler Yeats (author), Kenneth Branagh (actor)

Find the Words

R	D	K	G	U	I	N	N	E	S	S	E
H	S	E	X	U	K	E	L	L	S	L	Z
O	S	B	R	K	G	W	N	S	S	M	Y
G	O	E	T	R	Z	B	F	I	O	K	F
V	I	L	K	G	Y	F	D	S	R	Y	L
W	H	F	B	Z	I	L	O	O	X	S	N
C	I	A	W	L	A	D	C	T	K	S	I
Y	B	S	C	R	M	F	U	I	D	J	R
A	N	T	E	M	K	O	V	B	F	L	I
Y	G	M	M	B	D	P	H	F	L	C	S
N	E	M	F	P	C	G	O	E	B	I	H
M	H	J	U	Y	Z	D	A	G	R	D	N

BELFAST   EMERALD ISLE
CLIFFS   GUINNESS
CORK   IRISH
DERRY   KELLS
DUBLIN   MOHER

Country Flag

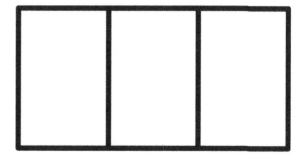

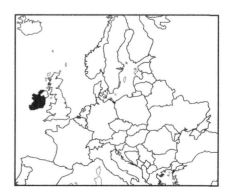

ITALY

National Motto: Union, Strength and Liberty!

Facts About Italy

Capital: Rome

Area: 116,348 square miles (301,340 square kilometers)

Major Cities: Venice, Florence, Milan

Population: 60,461,826

Bordering Countries: Austria, France, Holy See, San Marino, Slovenia, Switzerland

Language: Italian

Major Landmarks: Colosseum, Pantheon, Trevi Fountain, Mount Vesuvius, Leaning Tower of Pisa, Lake Como

Famous Italians: Leonardo da Vinci (Renaissance man), Julius Caesar (statesman), Christopher Colombus (explorer)

Find the Words

```
W G F L O R E N C E X W
G Z O C K T A I X F O P
F T L D M Y C P B P E O
G Q R N L I O K U A L N
C O L O S S E U M N C T
P V E L G N D N Q T O X
D A F V A E A P K H L Q
M X S Z E I L E V E O D
E K Z T L N M A G O M D
E I U A A O I Q T N B O
P Z T P R L K C H O U R
F I V A D K X F E G S E
```

COLOMBUS   PANTHEON
COLOSSEUM   PASTA
FLORENCE   PIZZA
GELATO   ROME
ITALIAN   VENICE

Country Flag

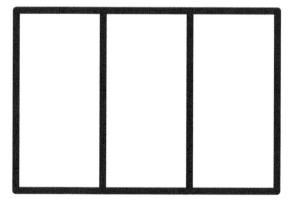

KAZAKHSTAN

National Motto: Freedom, Unity, Progress!

Facts About Kazakhstan

Capital: Nur-Sultan

Area: 1,052,100 square miles (2,724,900 square kilometers)

Major Cities: Almaty, Shymkent, Semey

Population: 19,074,790

Bordering Countries: Russia, China, Kyrgyzstan, Uzbekistan, Turkmenistan

Language: Kazakh, Russian

Major Landmarks: Bayterek, Kaindy, Medeo

Famous Kazakhstanians: Nursultan Nazarbayev (politician), Wladimir Klitschko (boxer), Al-Farabi (philosopher)

Find the Words

```
M N U C N I K A Z A K H
P O U D U A D U W Y X O
J L R N R G K O B Y S T
X W K M S O J P O M N K
Z C A E U E V O L E E G
S Y I D L W M U K R Y S
N L N E T R Z M E T Y L
A F D O A G Y T A D O D
Z S Y W N H Y M E Q L D
E W I J S A L B S B V X
M H I A B A M S E M E Y
H L A N D L O C K Q Y H
```

ALMATY	LANDLOCK
ASIA	MEDEO
BAYTEREK	NUR SULTAN
KAINDY	SEMEY
KAZAKH	SHYMKENT

Country Flag

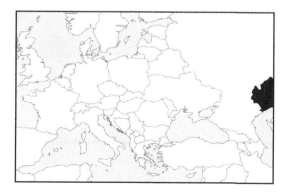

KOSOVO

National Motto: Honour, Duty, Homeland

Facts About Kosovo

Capital: Pristina

Area: 4,203 square miles (10,887 square kilometers)

Major Cities: Prizren, Peja, Mitrovica

Population: 4,935,259

Bordering Countries: Serbia, North Macedonia, Albania, Montenegro

Language: Albanian, Serbian

Major Landmarks: Mother Teresa Cathedral, Gracanica Monastery, Prizren's Fortress

Famous Kosovans: Era Istrefi (singer)

Find the Words

I	E	A	P	R	I	Z	R	E	N	M	F
I	N	L	L	Q	V	Q	G	A	C	I	X
S	N	D	N	B	A	T	N	J	J	T	Y
L	K	M	E	I	A	I	A	D	Y	R	B
A	E	B	B	P	T	N	B	S	S	O	A
M	A	R	C	S	E	X	I	D	F	V	L
G	E	W	I	G	P	N	R	A	C	I	K
S	C	R	B	T	N	E	D	C	N	C	A
K	P	O	G	J	Q	W	J	E	X	A	N
I	D	Q	T	R	A	Z	N	A	N	S	S
G	F	O	T	T	O	M	A	N	S	C	F
R	L	K	R	Z	I	W	V	T	J	U	E

ALBANIAN   OTTOMANS
BALKANS   PEJA
INDEPENDENCE   PRISTINA
ISLAM   PRIZREN
MITROVICA   SERBIA

Country Flag

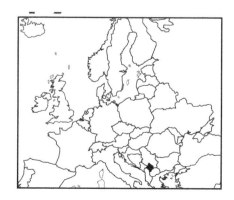

LATVIA

National Motto: For Fatherland and Freedom

Facts About Latvia

Capital: Riga

Area: 24,938 square miles (62,157 square kilometers)

Major Cities: Daugavpils, Ventspils, Jelgava

Population: 1,886,198

Bordering Countries: Estonia, Russia, Belarus, Lithuania

Language: Lettish

Major Landmarks: Rundāle Palace, Gauja National Park, Turaida Castle

Famous Latvians: Mikhail Baryshnikov (dancer), Isaiah Berlin (philosopher), Catherine I (monarch)

Find the Words

T	P	G	W	I	O	A	T	Q	O	Y	N
B	Z	M	I	K	J	W	G	A	U	J	A
Y	D	Z	H	A	B	A	L	H	D	Z	I
Y	N	T	P	W	E	T	E	C	J	B	Q
B	O	E	T	M	A	E	T	W	N	D	F
R	I	W	H	E	C	R	T	P	V	A	O
L	X	R	X	W	H	F	I	W	Z	V	R
Z	T	P	I	R	E	A	S	Q	E	N	E
W	W	S	D	G	S	L	H	P	S	H	S
A	Y	Q	K	W	A	L	Q	S	W	B	T
C	J	U	R	M	A	L	A	A	K	J	S
M	E	I	S	E	N	S	T	E	I	N	K

BEACHES   LETTISH
EISENSTEIN   LIEPAJA
FORESTS   RIGA
GAUJA   ROTHKO
JURMALA   WATERFALL

Country Flag

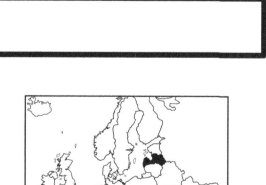

LIECHTENSTEIN

National Motto: For God, Prince and Fatherland

Facts About Liechtenstein

Capital: Vaduz

Area: 61.78 square miles (160 square kilometers)

Major Cities: Triesenberg, Schaan, Triesen

Population: 38,128

Bordering Countries: Switzerland, Austria

Language: German

Major Landmarks: Vaduz Castle, Alte Rheinbrucke, The Main Square

Famous Liechtensteiners: Josef Rheinberger (composer)

Find the Words

```
S C H E L L E N B E R G
L Y H N G J M R H I N E
A Y S Q R H O V A D U Z
L U C A A Q N K T C O M
P G H I U Z A J L A Z M
I V A B S O R Y R S J A
N J A N P L C E D T P L
E H N F I C H E D L U R
A T X R T O Y G J E M C
F R I I Z R W I O S P C
P R I N C I P A L I T Y
T R I E S E N B E R G C
```

ALPINE   RHINE
CASTLES   SCHAAN
GRAUSPITZ   SCHELLENBERG
MONARCHY   TRIESENBERG
PRINCIPALITY   VADUZ

Country Flag

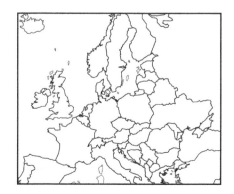

LITHUANIA

National Motto: Let unity flourish

Baltic
Sea

LATVIA

Mažeikiai

Būtingė
Šiauliai

Palanga
Panevėžys

Klaipėda

LITHUANIA
Utena

Kuršių
Kėdainiai

Jonava

Kaunas
VILNIUS

RUSSIA
Marijampolė   Lake Galvė

Alytus

POLAND
BELARUS

Facts About Lithuania

Capital: Vilnius

Area: 25,212 square miles (65,300 square kilometers)

Major Cities: Kaunas, Klaipeda, Siauliai

Population: 2,673,113

Bordering Countries: Latvia, Belarus, Poland, Russia

Language: Lithuanian

Major Landmarks: Trakai Island Castle, Hill of Crosses, Gates of Dawn

Famous Lithuanians: Emma Goldman (author), Jascha Heifetz (violinist)

Find the Words

```
B  E  H  U  K  A  U  N  A  S  V  K
N  E  M  A  N  R  I  V  E  R  A  R
L  O  T  Y  K  G  W  S  C  O  W  B
N  I  T  K  J  K  U  M  E  A  B  H
I  E  T  E  H  I  Z  Z  B  B  A  J
N  E  M  H  N  G  U  W  I  W  L  W
T  C  G  L  U  M  O  A  E  O  T  J
H  I  I  V  L  A  K  L  N  K  I  Q
F  V  H  E  Y  A  N  T  D  U  C  Y
O  E  T  F  R  Q  L  I  B  M  S  W
R  S  T  T  C  J  P  A  A  Y  A  X
T  V  P  A  L  A  N  G  A  N  M  N
```

BALTICS	NINTH FORT
GOLDMAN	PALANGA
KAUNAS	STELMUZE OAK
LITHUANIAN	TRAKAI
NEMAN RIVER	VILNIUS

Country Flag

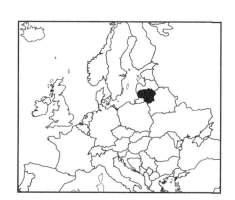

LUXEMBOURG

National Motto: We wish to remain what we are

Facts About Luxembourg

Capital: Luxembourg

Area: 998 square miles (2,586 square kilometers)

Major Cities: Dudelange, Differdange, Echternach

Population: 625,978

Bordering Countries: Belgium, France, Germany

Language: Luxembourgish, French, German

Major Landmarks: Mudam, Grand Ducal Palace, Neumünster Abbey

Famous Luxembourgers: Andy Schleck (cyclist), Hugo Gernsback (author)

Find the Words

```
C A S E M A T E S G H R
L L B L Y Y J W B R V E
X U K K J H Y E E A V C
S Y X L D H J G U N D H
J M L E T M N H N D I T
Q L A L M A G S E D F E
W H A L L B L E S U O R
O E J E L E O C C O N
W N D M N E E U O H S A
F U V N F J S Q R Y S C
D T U E D U L T C G L H
L T E T T E L B R U C K
```

CASEMATES   LUXEMBOURG
DUDELANGE   SMALLEST
ECHTERNACH   TUNNELS
ETTELBRUCK   UNESCO
GRAND DUCHY   WEALTHY

Country Flag

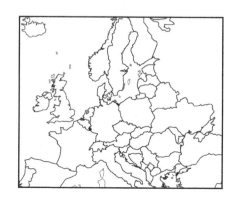

MALTA

National Motto: Strength and consistency

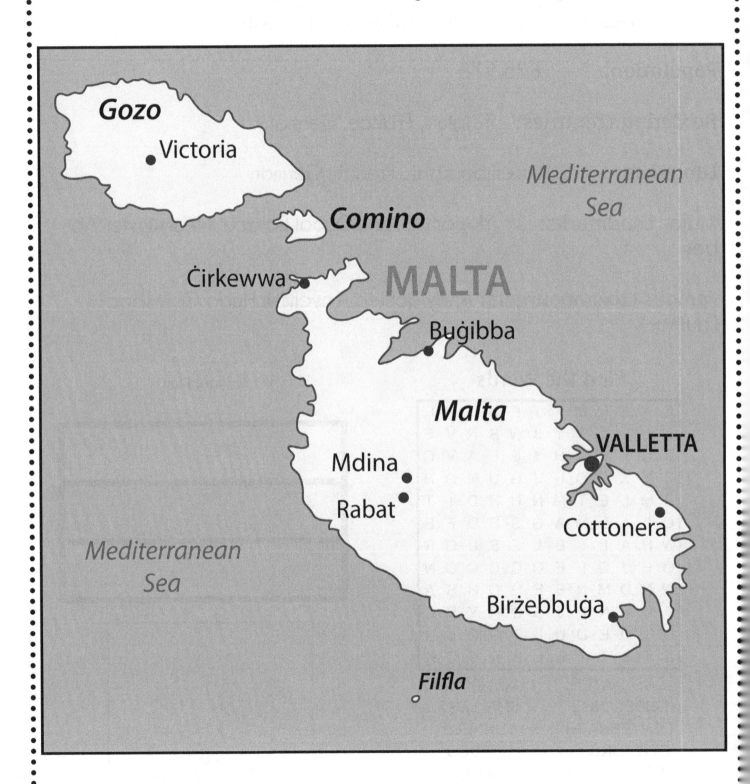

Facts About Malta

Capital: Valletta

Area: 122 square miles (316 square kilometers)

Major Cities: Mdina, Rabat, Qormi

Population: 441,543

Bordering Countries: None

Language: Maltese, English

Major Landmarks: Hypogeum of Paola, Mnajdra, Skorba Temples, Qawra Tower

Famous Maltese: Edward de Bono (psychologist), Joseph Calleja (singer)

Find the Words

```
A M Q N S H P J A V C W
R M J C Z A G M A A H P
C M A M O B V M G L I X
H M W L R M S T D L S W
I W D Y T I I N S E T W
P E I H R E A N P T O X
E K T U J L S K O T R F
L N O H S P A E D A I M
A T C I V O P O R O C V
G G E O R G E C R O S S
O S B L U E G R O T T O
J R A M L A B E A C H Z
```

ARCHIPELAGO	ISLAND
BLUE GROTTO	MALTESE
COMINO	RAMLA BEACH
GEORGE CROSS	TOURISM
HISTORIC	VALLETTA

Country Flag

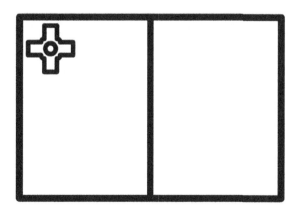

MOLDOVA

National Motto: No official motto

Facts About Moldova

Capital: Chişinău (Kishinev)

Area: 13,068 square miles (33,800 square kilometers)

Major Cities: Tiraspol, Balti, Orhei

Population: 4,033,963

Bordering Countries: Ukraine, Romania

Language: Romanian

Major Landmarks: Victory Memorial and Eternal Flame, Triumphal Arch, St. Teodora de la Sihla Church

Famous Moldavians: Vladimir Voronin (politician), Cleopatra Stratan (singer)

Find the Words

```
F P V T E I E O R H E I
L O K I A M T R T C P X
N R M R M O E X F H F B
T R S A G N R W N I B E
Z I H S M A N M E S I S
K D P P W S A L X I R S
A G W O Q T L E D N L A
E E U L H E F S V A I R
B A L T I R L W J U B A
C Y K J A I A R I R A B
M H H G V E M S E N Q I
F M T M C S E R R W E A
```

BALTI   MONASTERIES
BESSARABIA   ORHEI
BIRLIBA   PORRIDGE
CHISINAU   TIRASPOL
ETERNAL FLAME   WINE

Country Flag

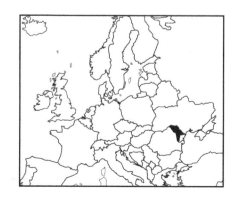

MONACO

National Motto: With God's help

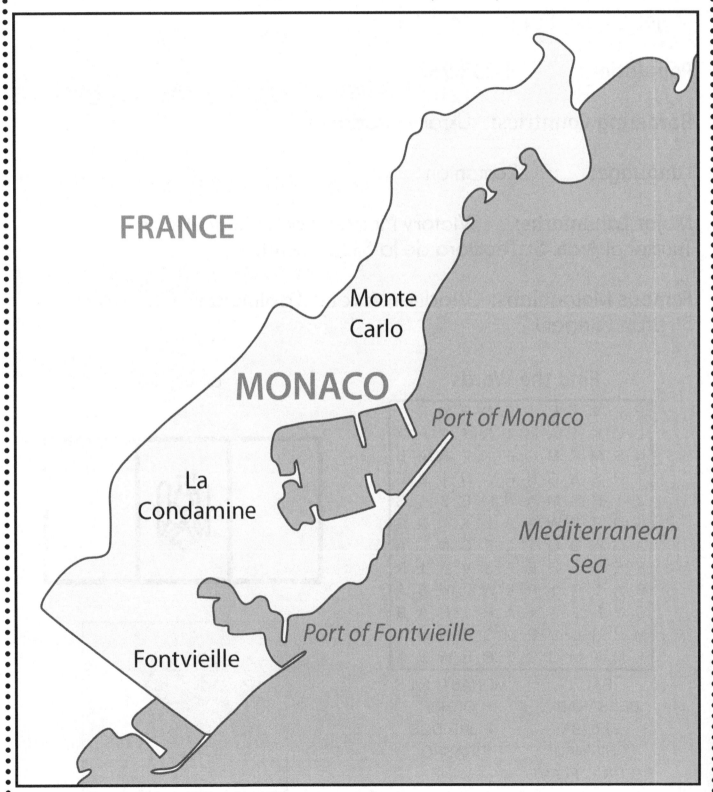

FRANCE

Monte
Carlo

MONACO

Port of Monaco

La
Condamine

Mediterranean
Sea

Port of Fontvieille

Fontvieille

Facts About Monaco

Capital: Monaco

Area: 499 acres

Major Cities: La Condamine

Population: 39,244

Bordering Countries: France

Language: French

Major Landmarks: Prince's Palace, Monaco Courthouse, Saint Nicholas Cathedral, Monte Carlo Casino

Famous Monégasques: Léo Ferré (artist), Albert II (prince)

Find the Words

```
W D Q P O M I N Q F P F
C Y P W C A S I N O A R
C A T H E D R A L S L E
G R A N D P R I X W A N
M O N T E C A R L O C C
K U N L Y W P C R R E H
P R I N C I P A L I T Y
W Y Z F R X K T K C L I
D Q A L P Z D Y S Y T T
F Q C I T Y S T A T E O
A Y Z R I V I E R A K S
Z L A C O N D A M I N E
```

CASINO   LA CONDAMINE
CATHEDRAL   MONTE CARLO
CITY STATE   PALACE
FRENCH   PRINCIPALITY
GRAND PRIX   RIVIERA

Country Flag

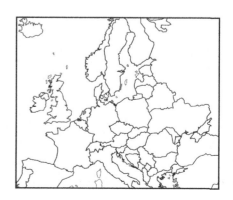

MONTENEGRO

National Motto: May Montenegro be eternal!

Facts About Montenegro

Capital: Podgorica

Area: 5,333 square miles (13,812 square kilometers)

Major Cities: Nikšić, Pljevlja, Herceg Novi

Population: 621,718

Bordering Countries: Croatia, Bosnia and Herzegovina, Serbia, Albania, Kosovo

Language: Montenegrin

Major Landmarks: Tare River Canyon, Kotor Old City, The Old Town, Biogradska Gora

Famous Montenegrins: Petar I (monarch)

Find the Words

T	A	R	A	R	I	V	E	R	R	H	P
B	B	H	T	S	W	R	H	O	D	E	O
A	W	O	E	O	Q	X	T	I	O	R	D
U	D	S	B	M	U	O	B	R	X	C	G
L	Y	R	O	O	K	R	G	F	N	E	O
C	M	B	I	F	T	E	I	D	G	G	R
I	L	B	O	A	N	O	K	S	T	N	I
N	A	Y	X	E	T	B	V	K	M	O	C
J	A	E	T	G	X	I	I	K	D	V	A
B	I	N	B	S	K	N	C	E	U	I	W
E	O	G	F	V	B	L	H	I	W	K	F
M	L	A	K	E	S	K	A	D	A	R	W

ADRIATIC	MONTENEGRO
BAY OF KOTOR	PODGORICA
BOBOTOV KUK	TARA RIVER
HERCEG NOVI	TOURISM
LAKE SKADAR	ULCINJ

Country Flag

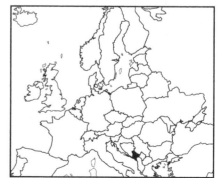

NETHERLANDS

National Motto: *I will maintain*

North Sea

Den Helder

Leeuwarden

Delfzijl

Groningen

Assen

NETHERLANDS

Zwolle

IJmuiden

Haarlem

AMSTERDAM

The Hague

Utrecht

Arnhem

Rotterdam

Europoort

Dordrecht

Nijmegen

Tilburg

GERMANY

Terneuzen

Eindhoven

BELGIUM

Maastricht

Facts About Netherlands

Capital: Amsterdam

Area: 15,907 square miles (41,198 square kilometers)

Major Cities: Rotterdam, The Hague, Utrecht

Population: 17,134,872

Bordering Countries: Germany, Belgium

Language: Dutch

Major Landmarks: Binnenhof, Castle De Haar, Circuit Zandvoort, Keukenhof

Famous Dutch: Vincent Van Gogh (artist), Rembrandt (artist), Baruch Spinoza (philosopher), M. C. Escher (artist)

Find the Words

A	W	V	V	C	U	T	R	E	C	H	T
M	C	L	A	V	A	U	T	H	R	S	K
S	J	U	V	N	Y	N	Z	O	Q	C	S
T	Q	H	F	H	G	D	A	A	B	L	Q
E	H	V	G	H	D	O	F	L	L	Z	S
R	A	D	M	B	L	R	G	I	S	P	H
D	G	M	M	A	H	T	M	H	I	D	O
A	U	E	Y	C	O	D	H	L	E	B	L
M	E	B	T	Q	N	J	U	P	F	H	L
D	R	U	D	I	V	T	C	R	V	G	A
G	D	Y	W	Z	T	B	N	U	F	W	N
R	O	T	T	E	R	D	A	M	V	X	D

AMSTERDAM ROTTERDAM
CANALS TULIPS
DUTCH UTRECHT
HAGUE VAN GOGH
HOLLAND WINDMILLS

Country Flag

NORTH MACEDONIA

National Motto: No official motto

Facts About North Macedonia

Capital: Skopje

Area: 9,928 square miles (25,713 square kilometers)

Major Cities: Bitola, Kumanova, Prilep

Population: 2,083,374

Bordering Countries: Bulgaria, Greece, Serbia, Kosovo, Albania

Language: Macedonian

Major Landmarks: Matka Canyon, Vrelo Cave, Stobi

Famous Macedonians: Ptoly I Soter (monarch)

Find the Words

U	M	A	C	E	D	O	N	I	A	N	N
Q	V	W	M	M	H	Y	Z	S	H	O	K
B	R	C	S	O	E	F	U	G	Y	O	P
I	E	X	T	Q	U	V	B	N	D	E	Z
T	L	E	A	Z	Y	N	A	U	L	U	S
O	O	A	C	G	S	C	T	I	C	U	T
L	C	C	Z	E	A	K	R	A	F	K	O
A	A	P	M	K	S	P	O	J	I	R	B
K	V	P	T	E	C	S	N	P	F	N	I
P	E	A	K	F	V	U	M	U	J	S	S
X	M	A	D	W	E	D	E	W	T	E	M
I	L	T	E	T	O	V	A	H	T	Q	H

BITOLA   PRILEP
LAKES   SKOPJE
MACEDONIAN   STOBI
MATKA CANYON   TETOVA
MOUNTAINS   VRELO CAVE

Country Flag

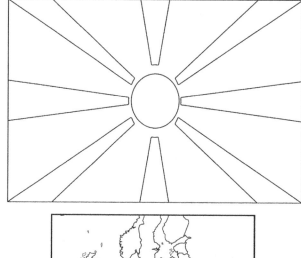

NORWAY

National Motto: No official motto

Facts About Norway

Capital: Oslo

Area: 148,718 square miles (385,178 square kilometers)

Major Cities: Bergen, Trondheim, Stavanger

Population: 5,421,241

Bordering Countries: Sweden, Finland, Russia

Language: Norwegian

Major Landmarks: North Cape, Preikestolen, Trolltunga, Geirangerfjord, Akershus Fortress

Famous Norwegians: Henrik Ibsen (playwright), Edvard Munch (artist), Fridtjof Nansen (scientist)

Find the Words

```
G L T R O L L T U N G A
W T I U G R F X V N S A
S R H L O Y D J E I I R
N O P D L Z X G O V Z B
O N Y U V E R X A R R L
R D P O T E H N A V D E
T H W R B E I A X I M S
H E V D N D T E M L W K
C I K O N N D F O M F R
A M R A D Q Q A I S E D
P K C N K G A R T C L R
E S N O R W E G I A N O
```

BERGEN   NORWEGIAN
FJORDS   OSLO
KRONE   SCANDINAVIA
LILLEHAMMER   TROLLTUNGA
NORTH CAPE   TRONDHEIM

Country Flag

POLAND

National Motto: For our freedom and yours

Facts About Poland

Capital: Warsaw

Area: 120,728 square miles (312,685 square kilometers)

Major Cities: Kraków, Łódź, Wrocław

Population: 37,846,611

Bordering Countries: Germany, Czech Republic, Slovakia, Ukraine, Belarus, Lithuania

Language: Polish

Major Landmarks: Poznań Fara, Wawel Castle, Malbork Castle, Wieliczka Salt Mine

Famous Polish: Marie Curie (scientist), John Paul II (pope), Nicolaus Copernicus (mathematician), Arthur Schopenhauer (philosopher)

Find the Words

W	O	A	U	M	Y	P	E	N	C	G	C
S	A	H	U	C	P	I	O	I	M	A	O
Y	D	W	N	Q	R	D	L	P	Y	P	P
K	Z	Q	E	U	P	O	E	O	E	W	E
R	H	M	C	L	H	O	L	K	A	R	R
A	L	B	W	T	C	W	L	S	L	Z	N
K	J	M	A	Z	Y	A	R	I	V	E	I
O	B	C	N	J	G	A	S	W	S	Q	C
W	P	K	D	O	W	C	H	T	U	H	U
A	L	M	A	L	B	O	R	K	L	R	S
D	J	S	K	L	Z	J	R	R	Z	E	X
D	I	D	G	D	A	N	S	K	W	K	W

CATHOLIC   MALBORK
COPERNICUS   POLISH
CURIE   POPE
GDANSK   WARSAW
KRAKOW   WAWEL CASTLE

Country Flag

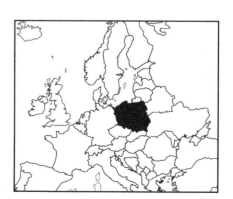

PORTUGAL

National Motto: No official motto

Facts About Portugal

Capital: Lisbon

Area: 34,183 square miles (88,146 square kilometers)

Major Cities: Porto, Coimbra, Braga

Population: 10,196,709

Bordering Countries: Spain

Language: Portuguese

Major Landmarks: Dom Luis Bridge, Benagil Sea Cave, Pena Palace

Famous Portuguese: Ferdinand Magellan (explorer), Cristiano Ronaldo (soccer player)

Find the Words

```
E X P L O R E R S W J G
B N J P B I S P O Z T U
R D R O E Q B G O E I N
A P G R N A Q E U R O M
G H B T A D L I R B T E
A G X U G Z E G S I R O
M U I G I Q P I A I A Z
E C V U L R L Z P R B N
X R R E S Q L M I M V P
V C Y S E A E B F K A E
J R O E A O H D I Q R V
P E N A P A L A C E O L
```

ALGARVE   IBERIAN
BENAGIL SEA   LISBON
BRAGA   PENA PALACE
EMPIRE   PORTO
EXPLORERS   PORTUGUESE

Country Flag

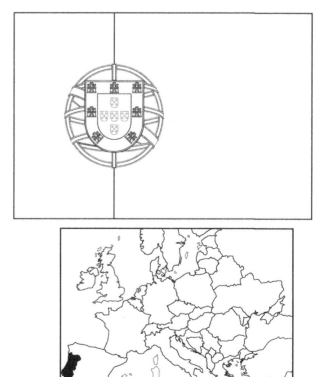

ROMANIA

National Motto: No official motto

Facts About Romania

Capital: Bucharest

Area: 92,046 square miles (238,397 square kilometers)

Major Cities: Iași, Timișoara, Cluj-Napoca

Population: 19,237,691

Bordering Countries: Ukraine, Moldova, Bulgaria, Serbia, Hungary

Language: Romanian

Major Landmarks: The Endless Column, Salina Turda, Bran Castle

Famous Romanians: Elie Wiesel (author), Nadia Comăneci (gymnast)

Find the Words

```
F S T W Y S G B Z B X C
H D R V V A C L L R R A
Y R A Z R L Q A S A O R
B A N H V I M C T N M P
R C S O F N Y K U C A A
A U Y Y D A U C N A N T
S L L H A T P H Q S I H
O A V R N U A U Q T A I
V N A T U R V R W L N A
K B N B B D A C E E F N
M Z I N E A M H L X U S
T W A B U C H A R E S T
```

BLACK CHURCH   DANUBE
BRAN CASTLE   DRACULA
BRASOV   ROMANIAN
BUCHAREST   SALINA TURDA
CARPATHIANS   TRANSYLVANIA

Country Flag

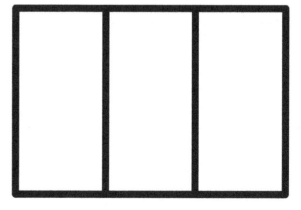

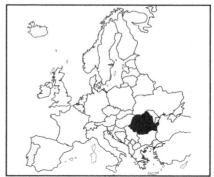

RUSSIA

National Motto: No official motto

Facts About Russia

Capital: Moscow

Area: 1,532,500 square miles (3,969,100 square kilometers)

Major Cities: Saint Petersburg, Yekaterinburg, Novosibirsk

Population: 145,934,462

Bordering Countries: North Korea, China, Mongolia, Kazakhstan, Azerbaijan, Georgia, Ukraine, Belarus, Latvia, Estonia, Finland, Norway

Language: Russian

Major Landmarks: St. Basil Cathedral, Winter Palace, Red Square, Hermitage Museum

Famous Russians: Sergei Rachmaninoff (composer), Anton Chekhov (playwright), Peter the Great (monarch), Vladimir Lenin (politician)

Find the Words

```
Q G F A J V B A F Q U J
V Z N I R V F X R W N I
R S O V I E T U N I O N
Y Q Q Y R L A R G E S T
S T P E T E R S B U R G
N T C O L D W A R A R S
V S T X G R M A V T U I
V O L G A R I V E R S B
W I J Z L E N I N K S E
C R A P B J K F B S I R
D J M O S C O W R W A I
Y W S T A L I N B H N A
```

COLD WAR   SIBERIA
LARGEST   SOVIET UNION
LENIN   ST PETERSBURG
MOSCOW   STALIN
RUSSIAN   VOLGA RIVER

Country Flag

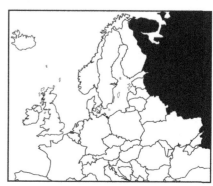

SAN MARINO

National Motto: Liberty

Facts About San Marino

Capital: San Marino

Area: 24 square miles (61 square kilometers)

Major Cities: Borgo Maggiore, Serravalle, Domagnano

Population: 33,931

Bordering Countries: Italy

Language: Italian

Major Landmarks: Rocca Guaita, Monte Titano, Basilica di San Marino

Famous Sammarinese: Massimo Bonini (soccer player)

Find the Words

```
T H R E E T O W E R S I
S M M E D I E V A L O F
E T I O M X W G C N A O
R S U C V I O N A S O R
R G A W R R T T L T O T
A U S N H O I A S P Q R
V A R X M T S E L K R E
A I V S E A T T T I P S
L T O T H A R M A Y A S
L A N R L H L I R T X N
E O D A S G T D N K E M
M B M D X B N Z K O S Q
```

FORTRESS   MICROSTATE
GUAITA   MONTE TITANO
ITALIAN   SAN MARINO
MALATESTO   SERRAVALLE
MEDIEVAL   THREE TOWERS

Country Flag

SERBIA

National Motto: Only Unity Saves the Serbs

Facts About Serbia

Capital: Belgrade

Area: 29,905 square miles (77,453 square kilometers)

Major Cities: Niš, Subotica, Kragujevac

Population: 8,737,371

Bordering Countries: Hungary, Romania, Bulgaria,
North Macedonia, Kosovo, Croatia, Bosnia and Herzegovina,
Montenegro

Language: Serbian

Major Landmarks: Vratna Gates, The Belgrade Fortress, Skadarlija

Famous Serbians: Novak Djokovic (tennis player), Constantine
the Great (emperor)

Find the Words

```
Z R N R V O K D B J S S
V Z A V F E O X L E B K
Z E A S B B L S T M E A
V U P U P V O A H N L D
T A N D N B G S N Q G A
T A M L N A E A G N R R
D G X P N W I R G Q A L
B O Q T I B Y Y R Y D I
R W A G R R P Y C I E J
C R D E M U E G A W E A
V X S Q B A L K A N S S
D E R D A P G O R G E P
```

BALKANS	RASPBERRIES
BELGRADE	SERBIAN
DANUBE	SKADARLIJA
DERDAP GORGE	VAMPIRE
KOLO	VRATNA GATES

Country Flag

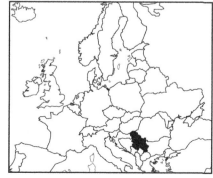

SLOVAKIA

National Motto: No official motto

Facts About Slovakia

Capital: Bratislava

Area: 18,933 square miles (49,036 square kilometers)

Major Cities: Košice, Nitra, Prešov

Population: 5,459,642

Bordering Countries: Poland, Ukraine, Hungary, Austria, Czech Republic

Language: Slovak

Major Landmarks: Spis Castle, Slovak Radio, Grassalkovich Palace, Bratislava Castle

Famous Slovaks: Martina Hingis (tennis player), Peter Sagan (cyclist)

Find the Words

```
N I T R A T P Q G O O P
L L S J M E C A D A M F
J W V P Y L X A V Q K O
Z A T X I Y L A V A Z L
T R V A M S L O V E P K
K H W P T S C O K T S D
C O M N I R L A U W N A
J L Q T K S A E S L Y N
E Z A F X J E S M T B C
B R Y Y L R C G D U L E
B A M O U N T A I N S E
J A W C A S T L E S Y D
```

BRATISLAVA   NITRA
CASTLES   SLOVAK
CAVES   SPIS CASTLE
FOLK DANCE   TATRAS
MOUNTAINS   WARHOL

Country Flag

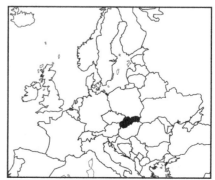

SLOVENIA

National Motto: No official motto

Facts About Slovenia

Capital: Ljubljana

Area: 7,827 square miles (20,273 square kilometers)

Major Cities: Maribor, Koper, Piran

Population: 2,079,303

Bordering Countries: Austria, Hungary, Croatia

Language: Slovenian

Major Landmarks: Predjama Castle, Lake Bled, Lipica Stud Farm, Postojna Cave, Triglav National Park

Famous Slovenians: Slavoj Žižek (philosopher), Tina Maze (skier)

Find the Words

```
S F P R E D J A M A L E
L L H B P U A N E B G X
O N J X M L V O J D Q O
V M T U F C I C I X M O
E A N C B A A R G A D E
N R V K Y L B S V S R X
I I J T O E J N T R Y T
A B A G L P N A H L B H
N O O P Q A E S N K E V
F R I H R E H R R A Y Y
A R M I M J R M M S G M
T Y P L A K E B L E D E
```

CASTLE   PIRAN
KOPER   PREDJAMA
LAKE BLED   SLOVENIAN
LJUBLJANA   TRIPLE BRIDGE
MARIBOR

Country Flag

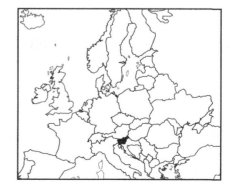

SPAIN

National Motto: Further beyond

ATLANTIC OCEAN

Bay of Biscay

FRANCE

La Coruna
Gijon
Bilbao
San Sebastian

ANDORRA

Vigo
Leon
Pamplona

Valladolid
Zaragoza
Barcelona

Salamanca
Segovia

MADRID

PORTUGAL

Tagus
Toledo

SPAIN

Valencia

BALEARIC
ISLANDS

Minorca

Mallorca

Olivenza
Albacete

Ibiza

Alicante

Cordoba

Huelva
Seville
Granada

Mojacar

Mediterranean Sea

Cadiz
Malaga
Almeria

Gibraltar (UK)

ATLANTIC
OCEAN

MOROCCO

ALGERIA

Facts About Spain

Capital: Madrid

Area: 192,476 square miles (498,511 square kilometers)

Major Cities: Barcelona, Seville, Granada

Population: 46,754,778

Bordering Countries: Portugal, France, Andorra

Language: Spanish

Major Landmarks: Camp Nou, Templo del Sagrado Corazon de Jesus, La Sagrada Familia

Famous Spanish: Pablo Picasso (painter), Fernando Torres (soccer player), Francisco Franco (politician)

Find the Words

```
E B A R C E L O N A R W
V G I B E R I A N H O Q
E W R M A D R I D F Y S
P S U A J N O Y Q W A O
I C H X N D H E Q N L Q
C Z W S A A L N U C P M
A X P R P L D O P E A R
S W P G I A N A F I L K
S L U V X P N U P D A T
O J E Y M B V I B C C X
E S V A N W R J S K E V
X E C D N V A Z T H W J
```

BARCELONA	PICASSO
CAMP NOU	PRADO
GRANADA	ROYAL PALACE
IBERIAN	SEVILLE
MADRID	SPANISH

Country Flag

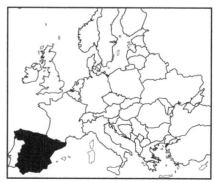

SWEDEN

National Motto: No official motto

Facts About Sweden

Capital: Stockholm

Area: 173,860 square miles (450,295 square kilometers)

Major Cities: Gothenburg, Malmo, Uppsala

Population: 10,099,265

Bordering Countries: Finland, Norway

Language: Swedish

Major Landmarks: Turning Torso, Svettekörka, Stockholm Cathedral, Drottningholm Palace

Famous Swedish: Ingrid Bergman (actress), Carl Linnaeus (botanist), Björn Borg (tennis player), Alfred Nobel (chemist)

Find the Words

```
S Y A M E A T B A L L S
F C G B E R G M A N S M
W W A M O O S E E E T J
P G U N Y G D O S Y O S
F K O P D C T I G A C W
V R P T R I A O S R K E
I O P E H K N T P K H D
T N X Q E E S A I Z O I
I A U N W E B K V G L S
Y Y B M R Y Q U Z I M H
Y E Y O X X K R R P A P
K M F Z P Z D W A G D F
```

BERGMAN   MEATBALLS
FORESTS   MOOSE
GOTHEBURG   SCANDINAVIA
KEBNEKAISE   STOCKHOLM
KRONA   SWEDISH

Country Flag

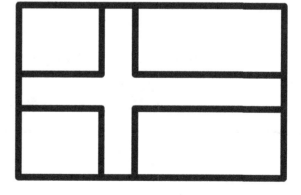

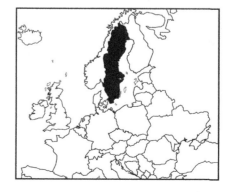

SWITZERLAND

National Motto: One for all, all for one

Facts About Switzerland

Capital: Bern

Area: 15,940 square miles (41,290 square kilometers)

Major Cities: Geneva, Lucerne, Basel

Population: 8,654,622

Bordering Countries: Italy, France, Germany, Austria

Language: German, French, Italian

Major Landmarks: Lake Geneva, The Matterhorn, Titlis, Rhine Falls

Famous Swiss: Jean-Jacques Rousseau (philosopher), Carl Jung (psychologist), Leonhard Euler (mathematician)

Find the Words

C	C	C	F	I	E	M	R	F	R	D	A
C	H	J	I	A	L	P	S	C	N	I	S
O	O	T	I	T	L	I	S	A	M	V	Q
E	C	G	B	L	I	D	L	F	W	M	J
G	O	K	E	F	U	R	R	M	D	L	S
F	L	E	U	N	E	C	N	W	E	M	K
D	A	V	R	Z	E	L	E	S	W	T	I
U	T	T	T	N	T	V	A	R	N	O	I
T	E	I	H	U	G	B	A	R	N	H	N
Q	W	I	B	T	H	H	E	G	Q	E	G
S	N	I	Y	N	X	B	H	K	S	U	K
J	K	M	A	T	T	E	R	H	O	R	N

ALPS   LUCERNE
BASEL   MATTERHORN
BERN   SKIING
CHOCOLATE   SWITZERLAND
GENEVA   TITLIS

Country Flag

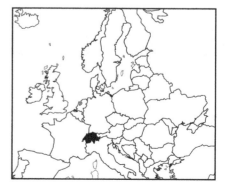

TURKEY

National Motto: No official motto

Facts About Turkey

Capital: Ankara

Area: 302,455 square miles (783,356 square kilometers)

Major Cities: Istanbul, Izmir, Antalya

Population: 85,513,784

Bordering Countries: Armenia, Azerbaijan, Bulgaria, Georgia, Greece, Iran, Iraq, Syria

Language: Turkish

Major Landmarks: Hagia Sophia, Blue Mosque, Grand Bazaar, Pamukkale, Temple of Artemis

Famous Turks: Paul the Apostle (religious leader), Suleiman the Magnificent (politician), Galen (physician)

Find the Words

```
R I B Y Z A N T I U M K
Q H A N T A L Y A S E S
I L A M N J N J B U T U
S B P G I S C H Q U Y L
T W A Y I A H S A E N E
A A Z Z X A O F I K H I
N M N Z A M S R E S X M
B A U K E A I O I V N A
U H F U A M R K P M P N
L J L H Z R R S C H J K
C B H I E U A E B F I Q
N K D A T E J V P R B A
```

ANKARA   HAGIA SOPHIA
ANTALYA   ISTANBUL
BAZAARS   IZMIR
BLUE MOSQUE   SULEIMAN
BYZANTIUM   TURKISH

Country Flag

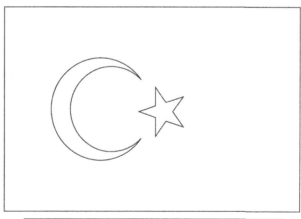

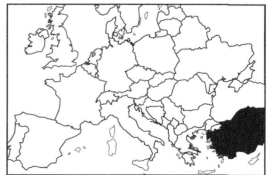

UKRAINE

National Motto: Glory to Ukraine! Glory to the heroes!

Facts About Ukraine

Capital: Kyiv

Area: 233,062 square miles (603,628 square kilometers)

Major Cities: Odesa, Lviv, Kharkiv

Population: 43,733,762

Bordering Countries: Belarus, Russia, Moldova, Romania, Hungary, Slovakia, Poland

Language: Ukrainian

Major Landmarks: Lake Svityaz, Askania-Nova, Probiy Waterfall, Livadia Palace

Famous Ukrainians: Leon Trotsky (revolutionary), Wladimir Klitschko (boxer)

Find the Words

```
B L A C K S E A P L C L
L T K U H L N W U I L A
C A D Y J D P M L T D R
O I K Y I F V B Y J X G
S K N E M V U G E P C E
S L H J S P W K J V O S
A L D A E V Q M L S A T
C V Y R R L I S G S G B
K I T U V K J T E O I E
S V R Q Z C I D Y K U O
C E W D J G O V O A K P
U K R A I N I A N A Z Q
```

BLACK SEA   LARGEST
COSSACKS   LVIV
KHARKIV   ODESA
KYIV   REPUBLIC
LAKE SVITYAZ   UKRAINIAN

Country Flag

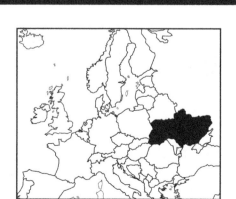

UNITED KINGDOM

National Motto: No official motto

Facts About United Kingdom

Capital: London

Area: 93,628 square miles (242,495 square kilometers)

Major Cities: Edinburgh, Glasgow, Birmingham

Population: 67,886,011

Bordering Countries: Ireland

Language: English

Major Landmarks: Blackpool Tower, Sherwood Forest, Big Ben, River Thames, Tower of London, Buckingham Palace

Famous British: Victoria (monarch), William Shakespeare (author), Winston Churchill (statesman), Charles Darwin (biologist)

Find the Words

```
N S T O N E H E N G E H
M U W A L E S B N Q N E
B B F E L B I G O P R W
S R N X L P W N K A C E
V I U S L O E O E D W D
W T T E C B N P N N I I
C I L Z G O S D E G C N
U S I I U E T E O V L B
N H B S K Y U L C N Y U
H R X A G Q M V A J S R
A B H C J K M N K N L G
A S J E N G L A N D D H
```

BIG BEN   QUEEN
BRITISH   SCOTLAND
EDINBURGH   SHAKESPEARE
ENGLAND   STONEHENGE
LONDON   WALES

Country Flag

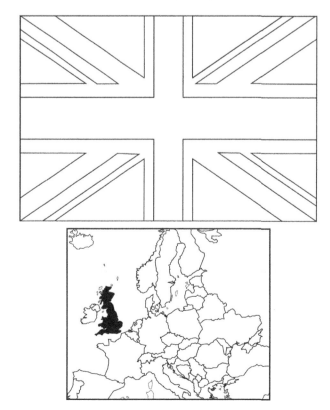

VATICAN CITY

National Motto: No official motto

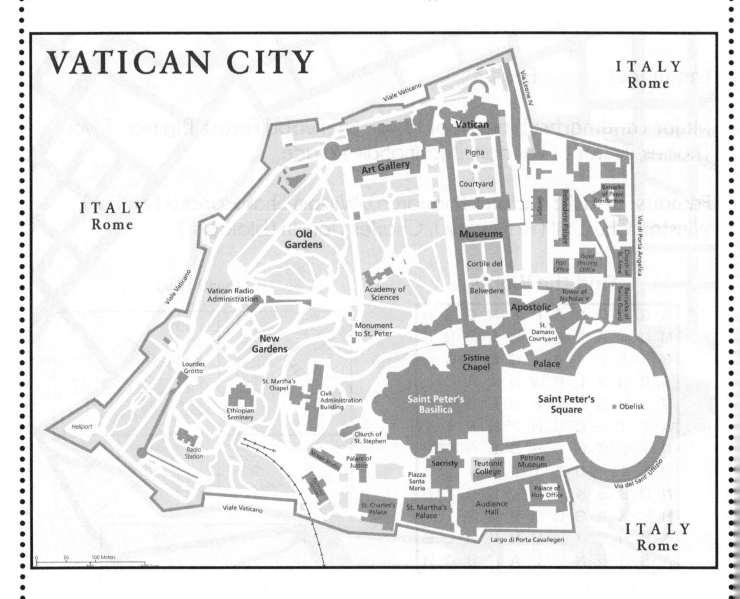

VATICAN CITY

ITALY
Rome

Viale Vaticano

Via Leone IV

Vatican

Pigna

Courtyard

Art Gallery

ITALY
Rome

Barracks
of Papal
Gendarmes

Old
Gardens

Museums

Belvedere Palace

Garage

Via di Porta Angelica

Church of
St. Anne

Post
Office

Papal
Printing
Office

Barracks of
Swiss Guard

Vatican Radio
Administration

Viale Vaticano

Cortile del

Academy of
Sciences

Belvedere

Tower of
Nicholas V

Apostolic

Monument
to St. Peter

St.
Damaso
Courtyard

New
Gardens

Lourdes
Grotto

Sistine
Chapel

Palace

St. Martha's
Chapel

Civil
Administration
Building

Saint Peter's
Basilica

Saint Peter's
Square

Obelisk

Ethiopian
Seminary

Heliport

Church of
St. Stephen

Radio
Station

Mosaic Studio

Palace of
Justice

Sacristy

Teutonic
College

Petrine
Museum

Via del Sant' Uffizio

Piazza
Santa
Maria

Palace of
Holy Office

St. Charles's
Palace

St. Martha's
Palace

Audience
Hall

ITALY
Rome

Viale Vaticano

Largo di Porta Cavallegeri

0   50   100 Meters

Facts About Vatican City

Capital: Vatican City

Area: 109 Acres

Major Cities: Vatican City

Population: 801

Bordering Countries: Italy

Language: Latin, Italian

Major Landmarks: Sistine Chapel, St. Peter's Basilica, Saint Peter's Square

Famous Vaticans: Pope Francis

Find the Words

```
M X B F S M A L L E S T
T I Y H N H O L Y S E E
S L C X P Z V Z B N I C
I A X H Y M X Z A O B I
L T B G E K U I I N Q T
P I A B B L L S A G F Y
A N S E L A A C E H S H
Y A I X T J I N D U P R
P A L I C T E C G J M H
V I I M A P Z V A E K S
F I C V O F B V N U L U
L V A P N M B L B T P O
```

BASILICA   MICHELANGELO
CITY   MUSEUMS
HOLY SEE   POPE
ITALIAN   SMALLEST
LATIN   VATICAN

Country Flag

Use the numbered map to fill in the names of the 51 countries below.

1. _____
2. _____
3. _____
4. _____
5. _____
6. _____
7. _____
8. _____
9. _____
10. _____
11. _____
12. _____
13. _____
14. _____
15. _____
16. _____
17. _____
18. _____
19. _____
20. _____
21. _____
22. _____
23. _____
24. _____
25. _____

26. _____
27. _____
28. _____
29. _____
30. _____
31. _____
32. _____
33. _____
34. _____
35. _____
36. _____
37. _____
38. _____
39. _____
40. _____
41. _____
42. _____
43. _____
44. _____
45. _____
46. _____
47. _____
48. _____
49. _____
50. _____
51. _____

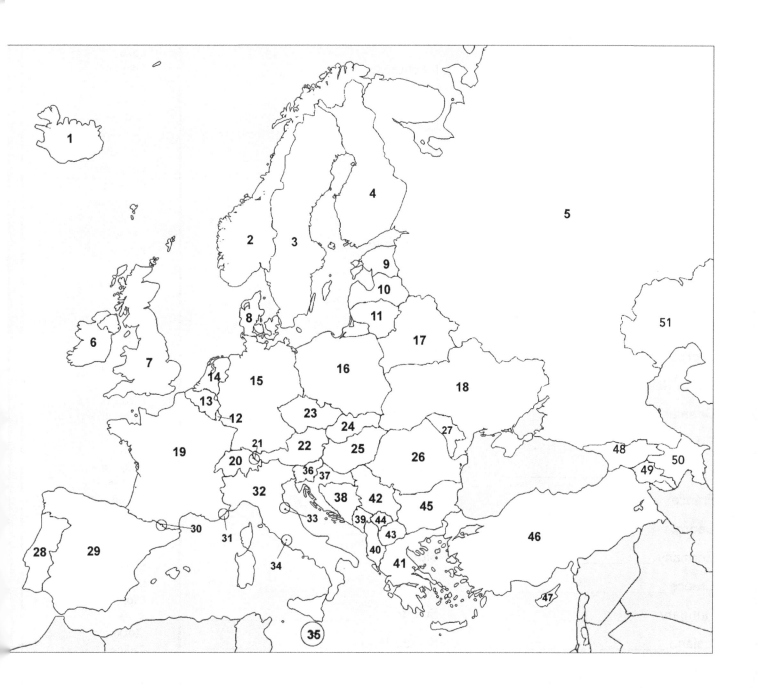

Country Capitals
Write the capital for each country.

Albania _____

Andorra _____

Armenia _____

Austria _____

Azerbaijan _____

Belarus _____

Belgium _____

Bosnia and Herzegovina _____

_____

Bulgaria _____

Croatia _____

Cyprus _____

Czech Republic _____

Denmark _____

Estonia _____

Finland _____

France _____

Georgia _____

Germany _____

Greece _____

Hungary _____

Iceland _____

Ireland _____

Italy _____

Kazakhstan _____

Kosovo _____

Latvia _____

Liechtenstein _____

Lithuania _____

Luxembourg _____

Malta _____

Moldova _____

Monaco _____

Montenegro _____

Netherlands _____

North Macedonia _____

Norway _____

Poland _____

Portugal _____

Romania _____

Russia _____

San Marino _____

Serbia _____

Slovakia _____

Slovenia _____

Spain _____

Sweden _____

Switzerland _____

Turkey _____

Ukraine _____

United Kingdom _____

Vatican City _____

Amsterdam
Andorra la Vella
Ankara
Athens
Baku
Belgrade
Berlin
Bern
Bratislava
Brussels
Bucharest
Budapest
Chisinau
Copenhagen
Dublin
Helsinki
Kyiv
Lisbon
Ljubljana
London
Luxembourg City
Madrid
Minsk
Monaco
Moscow
Nicosia
Nur-Sultan
Oslo
Paris
Podgorica
Prague
Pristina
Reykjavik
Riga
Rome
San Marino
Sarajevo
Skopje
Sofia
Stockholm
Tallinn
Tbilisi
Tirana
Vaduz
Valletta
Vatican City
Vienna
Vilnius
Warsaw
Yerevan
Zagreb

Answers

1. Five (Iceland, UK, Ireland, Malta, Cyprus)
2. Ukraine
3. Fourteen
4. Finland, France
5. Norway

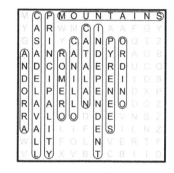
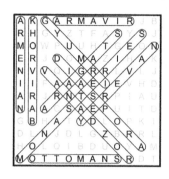
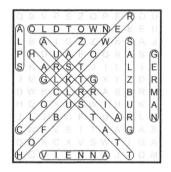

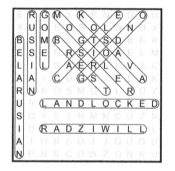
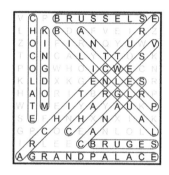

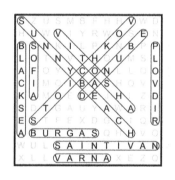
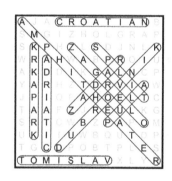
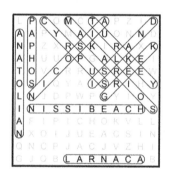
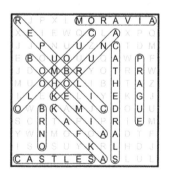
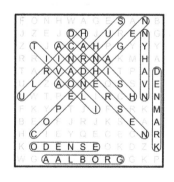

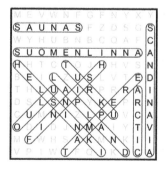
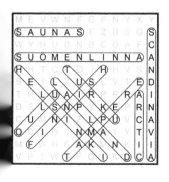

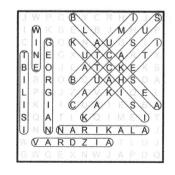
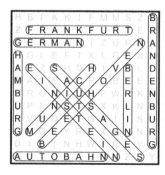

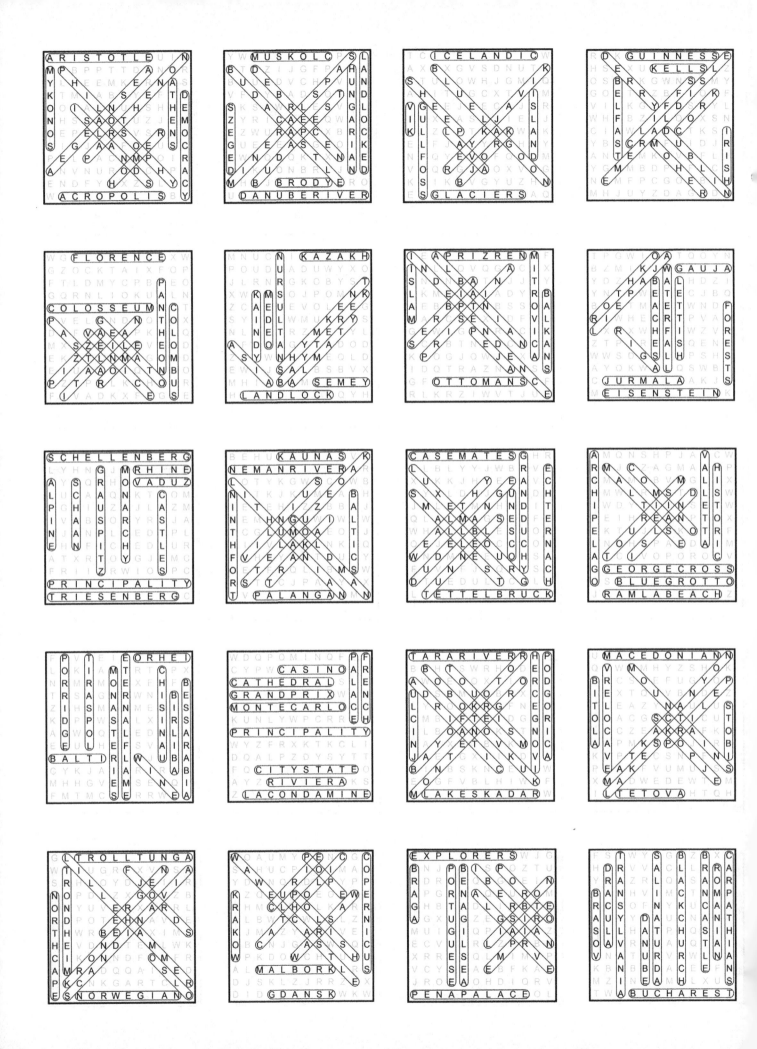

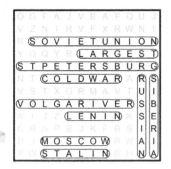
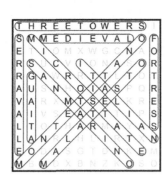

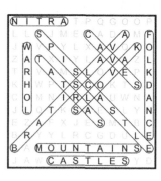
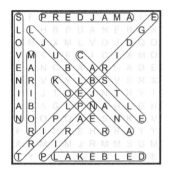

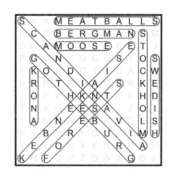
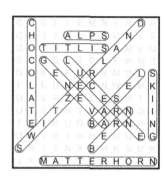

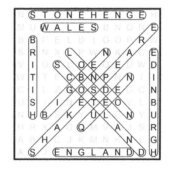
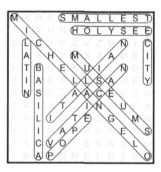

Albania	Tirana
Andorra	Andorra la Vella
Armenia	Yerevan
Austria	Vienna
Azerbaijan	Baku
Belarus	Minsk
Belgium	Brussels
Bosnia and Herzegovina	Sarajevo
Bulgaria	Sofia
Croatia	Zagreb
Cyprus	Nicosia
Czechia	Prague
Denmark	Copenhagen
Estonia	Tallinn
Finland	Helsinki
France	Paris
Georgia	Tbilisi
Germany	Berlin
Greece	Athens
Hungary	Budapest
Iceland	Reykjavik
Ireland	Dublin
Italy	Rome
Kazakhstan	Nur-Sultan
Kosovo	Pristina
Latvia	Riga
Liechtenstein	Vaduz
Lithuania	Vilnius
Luxembourg	Luxembourg
Malta	Valletta
Moldova	Chisinau
Monaco	Monaco
Montenegro	Podgorica
Netherlands	Amsterdam
North Macedonia	Skopje
Norway	Oslo
Poland	Warsaw
Portugal	Lisbon
Romania	Bucharest
Russia	Moscow
San Marino	San Marino
Serbia	Belgrade
Slovakia	Bratislava
Slovenia	Ljubljana
Spain	Madrid
Sweden	Stockholm
Switzerland	Bern
Turkey	Ankara
Ukraine	Kyiv
United Kingdom	London
Vatican City	Vatican City

Made in the USA
Monee, IL
16 February 2024

53627587R00063